MARVEL

AVENGERS

WELCOME

The Avengers need your help!

Using your Super Hero skills, search each
page of this book to try and uncover all
of the hidden objects. When you've found
them, go back through the book to complete
the bonus activities on the back pages
and break the secret code!

BADGE BUSTER

Look at this jumble of badges.
Can you find **8 badges** with
the red Avengers logo?

IRON MAN

Real Name: Anthony Edward Stark

Height: 6'1"- 6'5" in armour

Weight: 190 lbs / 425 lbs in armour

Bio: During a violent kidnapping at the hands of terrorists intent on forcing him to build a bomb, billionaire industrialist Tony Stark suffered a near fatal chest wound. Instead of the weapon that his captors had in mind, Stark constructed a sophisticated metal suit that both stabilised his injury and allowed him to escape. Upon returning home, he vowed to use his resources and intellect to protect the world as the armoured hero Iron Man!

POWERS & ABILITIES

- Stark is a genius with a talent for inventing
- Suit gives superhuman strength and the ability to fly
- Suit has artificial intelligence and other gadgets

CAPTAIN AMERICA

Real Name: Steven Rogers
Height: 6'2"
Weight: 230 lbs

Bio: During WWII, the frail but courageous Steve Rogers was injected with an experimental Super-Soldier Serum, emerging from the treatment as the pinnacle of human physical potential. Outfitted with a patriotic costume and iconic shield, he became the legendary Captain America! Though frozen in ice for decades after a climactic battle, Cap re-emerged in modern times, continuing the battle against evil as leader of the Avengers.

POWERS & ABILITIES

- Peak physical condition with boosted endurance
- Master in hand-to-hand combat
- Equipped with an indestructible Vibranium shield

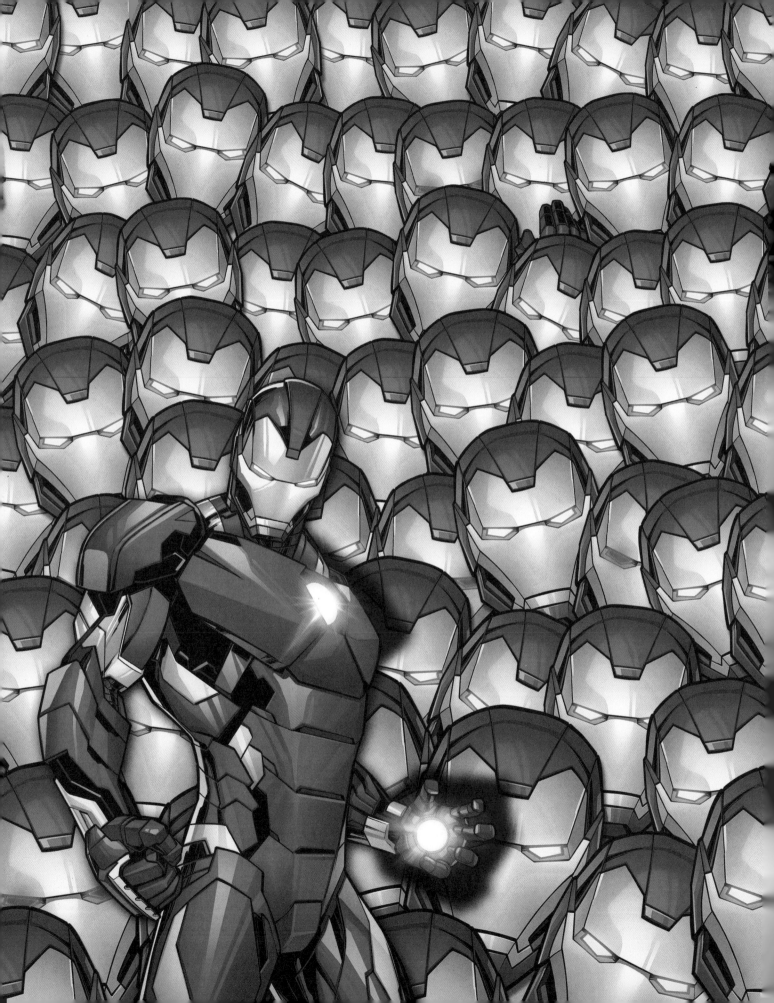

MASK MAYHEM

Some of Iron Man's helmets have a fault. Can you find **10 with glowing red eyes?**

Can you find Iron Man's glove on these pages?

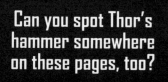

Can you spot Thor's hammer somewhere on these pages, too?

BATTLE READY

Before Cap can go into battle, he needs his shield. Can you find **10 shields with stars on?**

HULK

Real Name: Robert Bruce Banner
Height: 5'9" - 8'5" as Hulk
Weight: 145 lbs / 1040 lbs as Hulk

Bio: A massive dose of gamma radiation transformed the brilliant but meek scientist Bruce Banner into the green giant known as the Hulk. Often targeted by those who misunderstand him, Hulk prefers to use his immense power to smash the forces of evil, proving to the world that he is the strongest hero there is!

POWERS & ABILITIES

- Banner has a genius intellect and science expertise
- Hulk becomes more powerful the angrier he gets
- Hulk has superhuman strength and heals quickly

HULKBUSTER

Real Name: N/A
Height: 11'
Weight: 2500 lbs

Bio: Fearing the day when the Hulk's rage might become too much to control, Tony Stark developed the Hulkbuster as a countermeasure to Hulk's brute strength. The Hulkbuster armour encases Iron Man's normal suit, giving it an ultra-tough outer shell that allows it to withstand even the brute strength of the Hulk.

POWERS & ABILITIES

- Grants the wearer with superhuman strength
- Fully equipped for flight
- Can be remotely assembled and summoned on demand

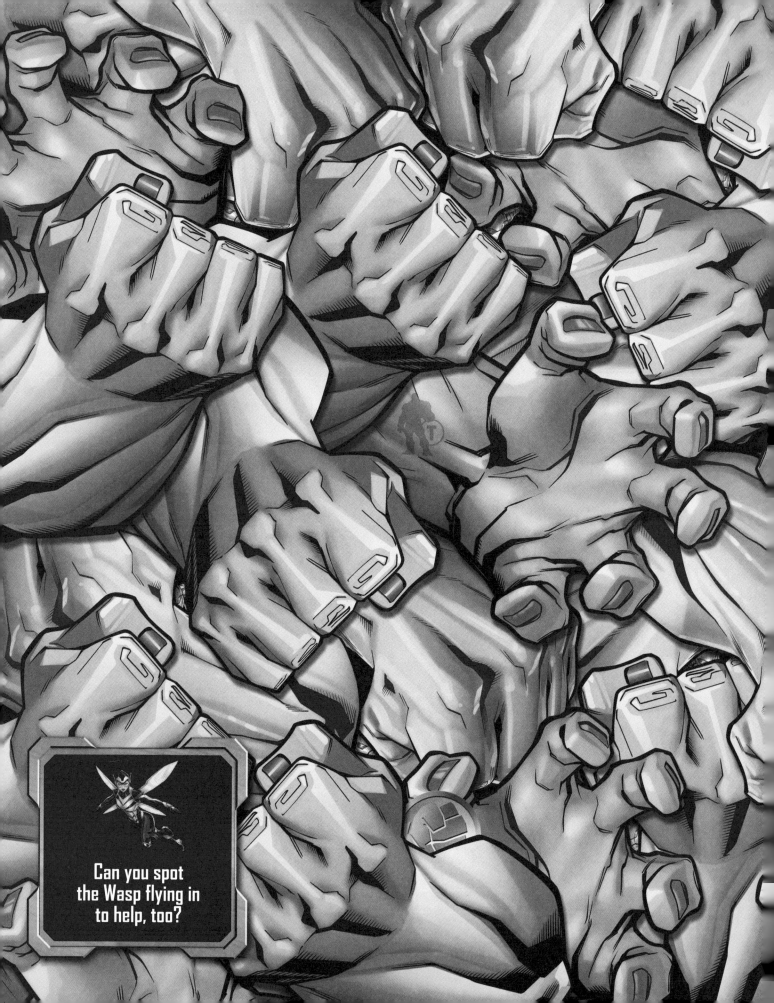

Can you spot
the Wasp flying in
to help, too?

HULK SMASH!

Ant-Man has made Hulk angry, but he's too small to catch! Can you spot him **10 times on these pages**?

Can you spot the ant hiding somewhere on these pages, too?

HEADS UP

Tony Stark is in the Hulkbuster suit but there's a fault. Can you find **10 radioactive symbols** on these pages?

MACH 0.16

1004

103 00013

ANT-MAN

Real Name: Scott Edward Harris Lang
Height: 6'
Weight: 180 lbs

Bio: Former thief Scott Lang once stole an advanced size-altering suit in order to aid his ailing daughter, only to discover that the stolen tech belonged to the world-renowned Dr Hank Pym. Seeing the heroic potential in Scott, Dr Pym allowed him to continue using the suit as well as the identity Pym once battled under. As the astonishing Ant-Man, Scott now handles the jobs 'too small' for any other Super Hero.

POWERS & ABILITIES

- Can shrink to a tiny size, while keeping strength
- Can communicate telepathically with ants
- Has an advanced knowledge of electronics

WASP

Real Name: Hope Van Dyne
Height: 5'4"
Weight: 110 lbs

Bio: With the unique ability to shrink in size and fly, Hope Van Dyne is the newest heroine to bear the name Wasp. Along with her partner, Scott Lang, Wasp battles evil on any scale, proving that true heroism comes in even the smallest of sizes.

POWERS & ABILITIES

- Can shrink to a tiny size, while keeping strength
- Can fly at high speeds using her wasp wings
- Can discharge powerful electronic bursts

COLONY CHAOS

Ant-Man and his ant army are going into battle. Can you find **10 arrows** hidden in the picture?

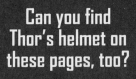

Can you find Thor's helmet on these pages, too?

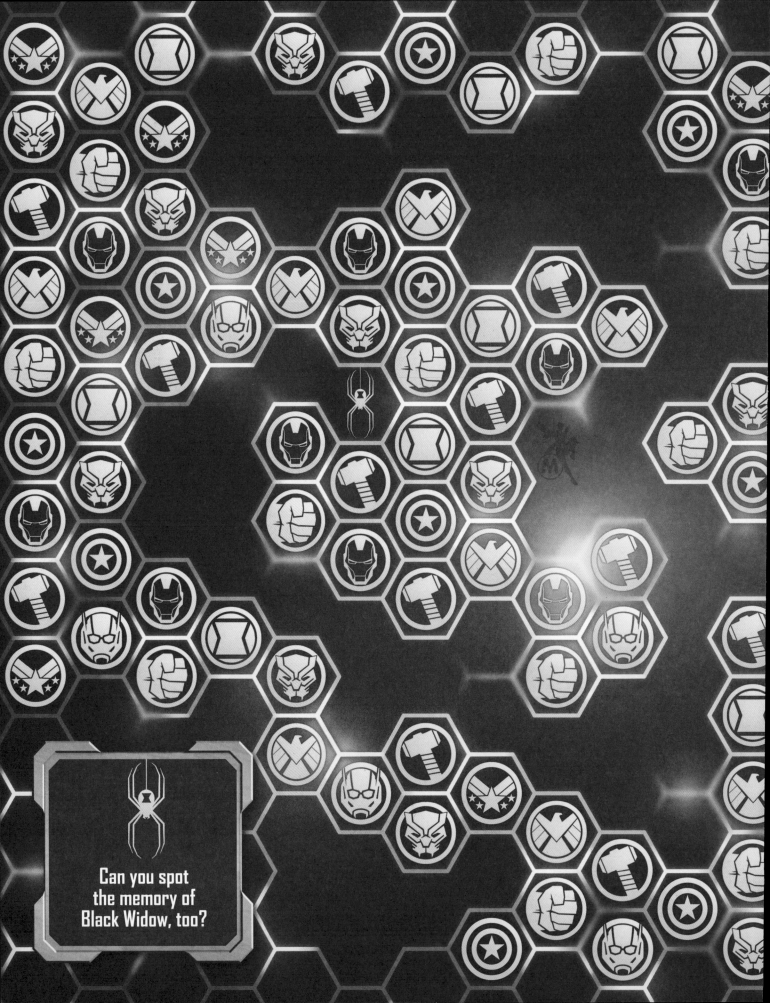

Can you spot
the memory of
Black Widow, too?

MEMORY MATCH

Wasp is searching her memory bank for Ant-Man. Can you find **10 discs** with his image on?

RED SKULL

Real Name: Johann Schmidt
Height: 6'1"
Weight: 195 lbs

Bio: The same Super-Soldier Serum that transformed Steve Rogers into Captain America during WWII also gave Hydra mastermind Johann Schmidt enhanced strength and stamina. However, an imperfection in the process caused Schmidt's face to become hideously disfigured, morphing it into a chilling skull. From that day forward, Schmidt was known as Red Skull and he and his army clashed with Captain America many times during the course of the war.

POWERS & ABILITIES

- Heightened strength, endurance and agility
- Skilled military leader and strategist
- Has access to an army and advanced weaponry

TRICK TIME

Red Skull has cloned Cap's shield to trick him. Can you find the **8 shields** hidden on this page?

BLACK WIDOW

Real Name: Natasha Romanoff
Height: 5'7"
Weight: 130 lbs

Bio: Raised from an early age in the top secret Red Room project, Natasha Romanoff was trained to be the Black Widow, a dangerous super-spy and master in the art of espionage and combat. Ultimately, she defected from her original keepers, instead seeking to right the wrongs of her past by joining the covert intelligence agency S.H.I.E.L.D.. Now, as a member of the heroic Avengers, Black Widow uses her unequalled skills to protect the innocent.

POWERS & ABILITIES

- Master in the art of combat and espionage
- Exceptional agility and athletic ability
- Has access to an array of advanced weaponry

CAPTAIN MARVEL

Real Name: Carol Danvers
Height: 5'11"
Weight: 155 lbs

Bio: A chance encounter with an alien being granted ace U.S. Air Force pilot Carol Danvers incredible powers. Endeavouring to use her fantastic new abilities for the forces of good, Danvers joined the Super Hero community in their ongoing struggle against evil. After years served protecting the planet, she began a new chapter in her heroic story when she took on the legendary mantle of Captain Marvel, Earth's mightiest hero!

POWERS & ABILITIES

- Superhuman strength, stamina and durability
- Flies at high speed and projects intense energy blasts
- Can transform into a powerful alternate form known as Binary

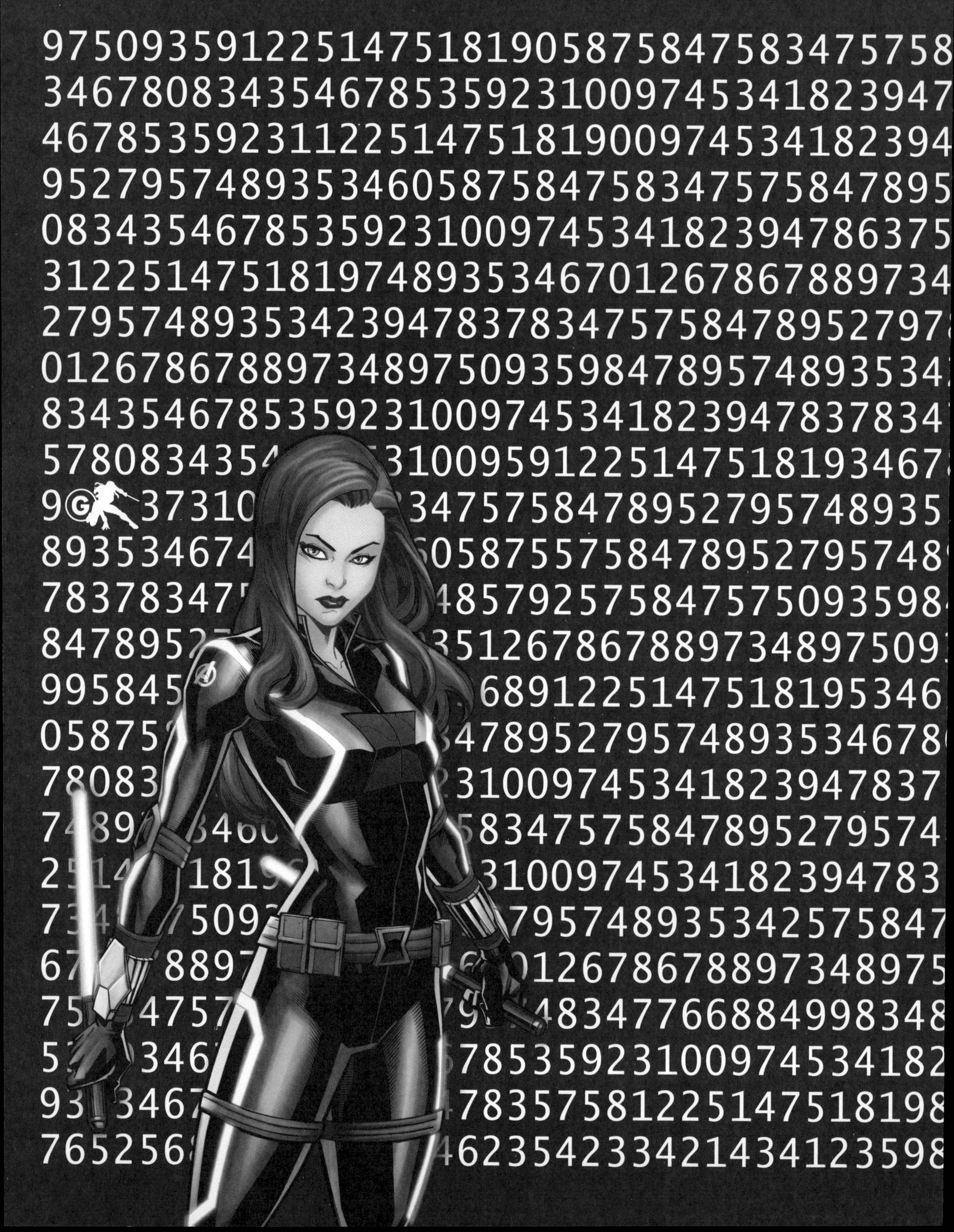

CODEBREAKER

Black Widow needs to hack an enemy system. Can you find the following **number pattern 10 times?**

1225147518119

```
895279574893
753467808340
378347575848
957489353467
635923100948
750935984789
5279574893534657489353468935346701267
9473783475758279389374534122514751819
2310758478952795748935346701297348553
8423106785368945923100974534182394723
6701267867889757584789527957895279574
5780834354678535923100974534182395984
9574891225147518193534239478378347575
9847894231009783756702394783789989978
1267867889734897509359847895279574893
3435467853592312251475181939478375346
4757584935342394783783475758478952795
3534678083435467853592310097453418212
3475758478952795748935346701267867889
9527957489353468935346701.2
9359847895279574893058758.4
345416823122514751811954678
9478378347575847895279574.8
973489750888984897489.31234
708534634634632367324.01258762
```

Can you find this Hawkeye logo on these pages, too?

STARGAZER

Captain Marvel has discovered a pattern in the stars. Can you find this pattern **10 times** in the picture?

Can you spot Black Widow's stun baton, too?

VISION

Real Name: Vision
Height: 6'3"
Weight: 300 lbs

Bio: Originally created by the evil robot Ultron to lure the Avengers into a trap, the synthetic being known as Vision found that he had more humanity than his creator intended. Relating to the human plight, Vision rebelled against his robotic master, choosing to put his fantastic powers to use for the good of mankind.

POWERS & ABILITIES

- Superhuman strength, speed and stamina
- Can shoot an energy beam from the jewel in his head
- Superhuman intelligence for advanced calculations

FALCON

Real Name: Samuel Thomas Wilson
Height: 6'
Weight: 170 lbs

Bio: Born and raised in Harlem, New York, Sam Wilson was an intelligent and adventurous child who possessed a great affinity for birds. Later, after excelling at the top of his class at S.H.I.E.L.D., a chance encounter with the legendary Captain America brought out his inner hero. When the call came for him to join the Avengers, he didn't hesitate and donned the hi-tech winged suit and became Falcon.

POWERS & ABILITIES

- Suit allows him high-speed flight and agility
- Master in the art of hand-to-hand combat
- Highly intelligent and has expertise in technology

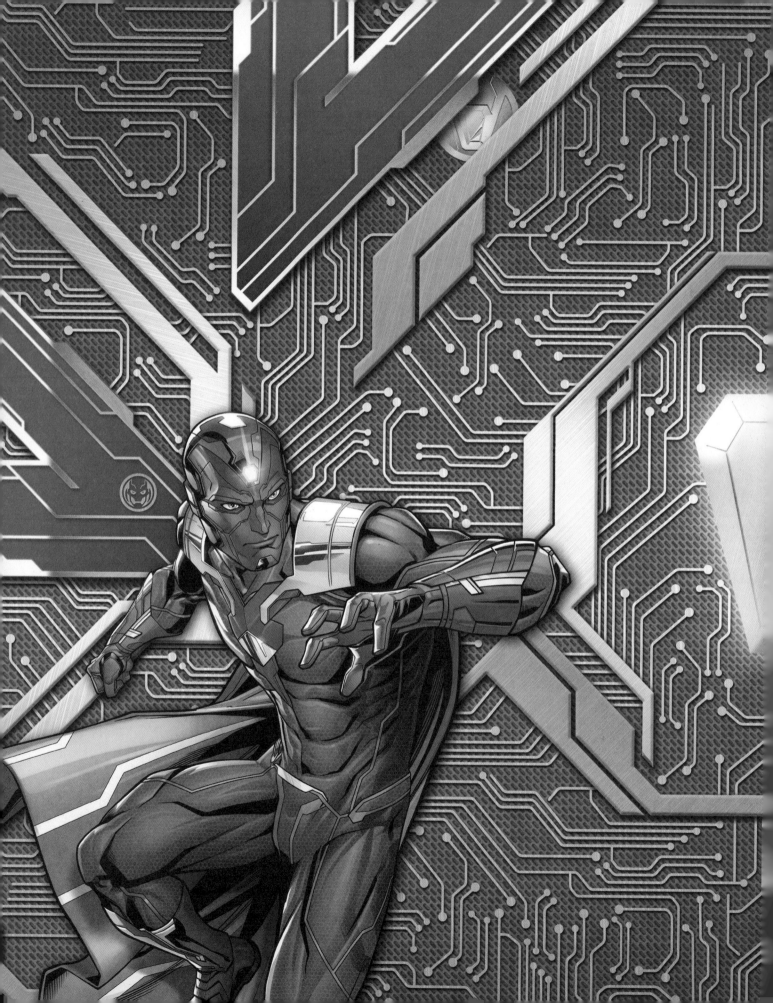

FAULT FINDER

Vision has a virus in his circuits. Can you find **10 circuits** that match the image?

Can you spot Ultron's virus mark on these pages, too?

LOGO LOCO

The S.H.I.E.L.D. logo is lost in this jumble. Can you help find **10 S.H.I.E.L.D. logos** on these pages?

Can you spot the Hulkbuster glove on these pages, too?

WAR MACHINE

Real Name: James Rupert Rhodes
Height: 6'1" - 6'6" in armour
Weight: 200 lbs / 475 lbs in armour

Bio: U.S. Air Force Colonel James 'Rhodey' Rhodes has long served as both Tony Stark's best friend and special liaison to Stark Industries. In battle, Rhodey dons the War Machine armour, a modified version of Stark's own Iron Man suit. Armed with a modular Gatling cannon and enough firepower to take on a legion of enemies, the War Machine is a true one-man army.

POWERS & ABILITIES

- The ability to fly, as well as superhuman strength
- Fully battle ready with a built in Gatling cannon
- Expert hand-to-hand combatant

PARTS PILE-UP

War Machine's spare parts pile is out of control! Can you spot **8 helmets** amongst the jumble?

LOKI

Real Name: Loki Laufeyson
Height: 6'4"
Weight: 525 lbs

Bio: Raised in Asgard alongside Thor, Loki's feelings of jealousy towards his noble foster brother ultimately turned his innate mischievousness to true evil. Ever seeking to challenge his brother's virtuous deeds, Loki uses his talents for manipulation and trickery in an obsessive quest to rule both Asgard and Earth. Caring for nothing but the rewards of his own schemes, Loki will lie, cheat and take any immoral action necessary to prove himself superior to other Asgardians.

POWERS & ABILITIES

- Superhuman strength, speed and endurance
- Member of the otherworldly Jotun race
- Master of reality manipulation and shape-shifting

MISCHIEF MAKER

Loki is up to his old tricks again. Can you find **8 replica Cosmic Cubes** on this page?

HAWKEYE

Real Name: Clinton Francis Barton
Height: 6'
Weight: 185 lbs

Bio: Trained from an early age in the art of archery, the young Clint Barton's skills earned him the nickname Hawkeye. Over time, Barton became one of the world's most elite marksmen. Inspired by the selfless deeds of Super Heroes like Iron Man and Captain America, Barton donned an iconic costume and put his sharpshooting skills to work as the heroic Hawkeye.

POWERS & ABILITIES

- Master marksman with near-perfect aim
- Utilises a unique bow and quiver of trick arrows with a variety of effects
- Expert hand-to-hand combatant, athlete and acrobat

ARROW ACTION

Hawkeye's arrows are in a mess. Help him find **8 arrows with green tips.**

THOR

Real Name: Thor Odinson
Height: 6'6"
Weight: 640 lbs

Bio: Legend tells of the son of Odin, heir to the otherworldly throne of Asgard - he is Thor, the mightiest hero of mythology. Once banished to Earth by his father Odin in order to learn a lesson in humility, the noble Thor has since vowed to protect the planet, using his enchanted hammer and mastery of the storm to vanquish any foes that threaten his adopted home.

POWERS & ABILITIES

- Superhuman strength and resistance to injury
- Wields the enchanted hammer, Mjolnir
- Master of the elements of thunder and lightning

DOCTOR STRANGE

Real Name:

Stephen Vincent Strange

Height: 6'1"

Weight: 180 lbs

Bio: Distinguished neurosurgeon Dr. Stephen Strange's self-important view was shattered along with his steady operating hands in a car accident. Desperate to heal his injuries and his pride, Strange sought out a legendary sage known as the 'Ancient One', becoming a pupil of the mystic arts. Learning that his true worth had always come from within, Strange was given the honour of becoming the Sorcerer Supreme.

POWERS & ABILITIES

- Master of the mystic arts
- Able to cast spells, enchantments and teleport
- Has access to an array of mystical antiques, each possessing untold powers and abilities

HAMMER TIME

Thor's hammer can fly at twice the speed of sound! Can you find **10 Loki helmets** on these pages?

Can you spot Cap's shield somewhere on these pages, too?

PORTAL PROBLEMS

Help Doctor Strange save Captain Marvel by finding her **10 times** on these pages.

Can you spot Hawkeye's arrow on these pages, too?

NICK FURY

Real Name: Nicholas Joseph Fury
Height: 6'3"
Weight: 210 lbs

Bio: Nick Fury has proudly saved the world many times over the years – as a U.S Army sergeant, as a tech-savvy super-spy and as Director of the world's most elite intelligence organisation, S.H.I.E.L.D.. Though always reliable, Fury typically works in secret, orchestrating events and communications and working solely with those that he trusts the most. Fury will always come out fighting when the forces of good are backed up against a wall.

POWERS & ABILITIES

- Master in espionage and strategy
- Utilises S.H.I.E.L.D.'S most advanced technology
- Expert hand-to-hand combatant

WINTER SOLDIER

Real Name:
James Buchanan 'Bucky' Barnes
Height: 5'10"
Weight: 195 lbs

Bio: Bucky Barnes served with honour in WWII alongside his partner and friend, Captain America. Presumed M.I.A towards the end of the war, Bucky had in fact been recovered by enemy agents who subjected him to a series of experiments. Bucky was reborn as the Winter Soldier, a covert agent who could be 'activated' when needed. Now working for good, Bucky is trying to atone for his bad deeds.

POWERS & ABILITIES

- Master marksman and covert strategist
- Equipped with a cybernetic arm that increases strength, power and response
- Expert hand-to-hand combatant

FILING FIASCO

Fury needs to gather all S.H.I.E.L.D. intel on Red Skull. Can you find **10 folders** with these symbols on?

Can you spot Hawkeye's bow on these pages, too?

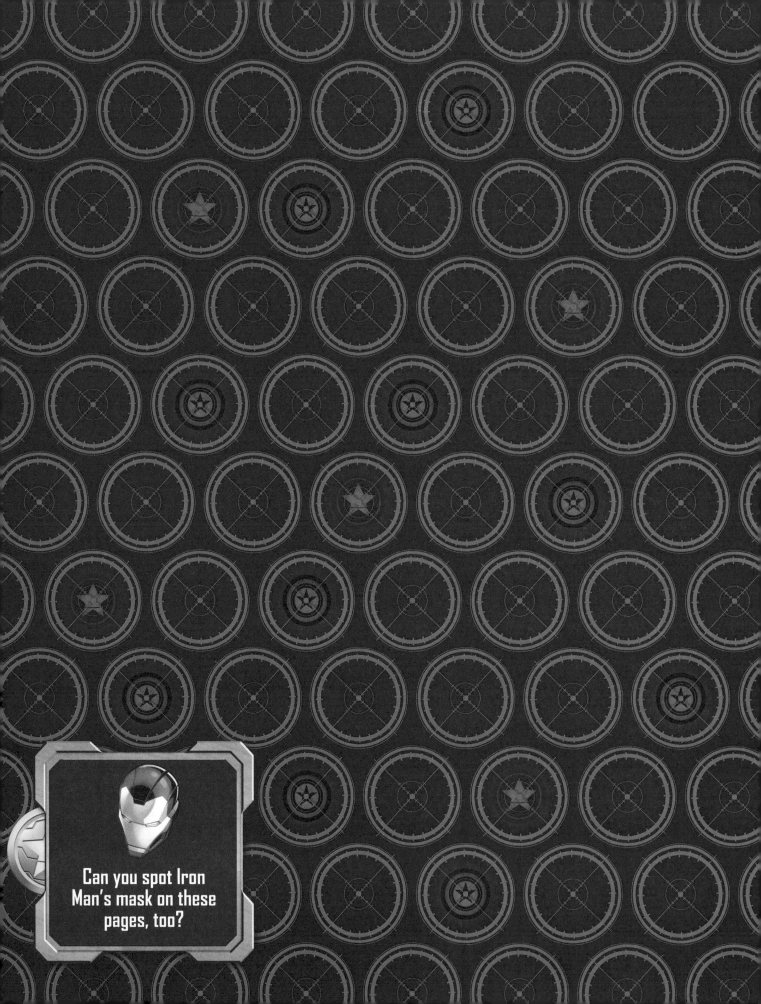

Can you spot Iron Man's mask on these pages, too?

TARGET PRACTICE

The Winter Soldier needs to hit the right targets. Can you find **10 red stars** on these pages?

BLACK PANTHER

Real Name: T'Challa
Height: 6'
Weight: 195 lbs

Bio: Monarch of the secluded but technologically advanced African nation of Wakanda, King T'Challa is the Black Panther, a sacred title that must both be inherited and earned by the current Wakandan ruler. Granted superhuman powers by ceremonially consuming a mystical heart-shaped herb, the Black Panther is responsible for defending his people and the world from any threats.

POWERS & ABILITIES

- Heightened strength, speed and stamina
- Master of martial arts and acrobatics
- Genius level intellect with expertise in physics

SHURI

Real Name: Shuri
Height: 5'5'
Weight: 130 lbs

Bio: Princess of Wakanda and T'Challa's sister, Shuri is a fierce warrior. When T'Challa has to leave Wakanda, he entrusts Shuri with the Black Panther title until his return.

POWERS & ABILITIES

- Heightened strength, speed and stamina
- Master of martial arts and acrobatics
- Utilises sophisticated Wakandan technology

OKOYE

Real Name: Okoye
Height: 5'9'
Weight: 150 lbs

Bio: Head of the Dora Milaje, a ceremonial order of warrior women, Okoye protects her king and her people fiercely.

POWERS & ABILITIES

- Peak physical condition with boosted endurance
- Master in hand-to-hand combat
- Skilled in the use of advanced Wakandan weapons

PANTHER PATTERNS

Wakanda forever! Can you spot **10 Black Panther logos** on these pages?

Can you spot the Avengers logo on these pages, too?

WEAPON WOES

There are spears everywhere!
Can you spot **10 Thor helmets**
hidden on these pages?

Can you spot Loki's
staff hidden on these
pages, too?

ULTRON

Real Name: Ultron
Height: Variable
Weight: Variable

Bio: Originally programmed to aid mankind, the A.I. known as Ultron decided that the best way to help mankind was to make them extinct. Acting upon his terrible plan, the Super Villain has proved himself to be an extremely dangerous foe, capable of infiltrating virtually any computer network. Even when defeated, Ultron can be 'reborn' if even a trace of his code is left intact.

POWERS & ABILITIES

- Can inhabit virtually any computer system
- Has increased strength and stamina in robotic form
- Possesses the ability to fly and shoot energy blasts

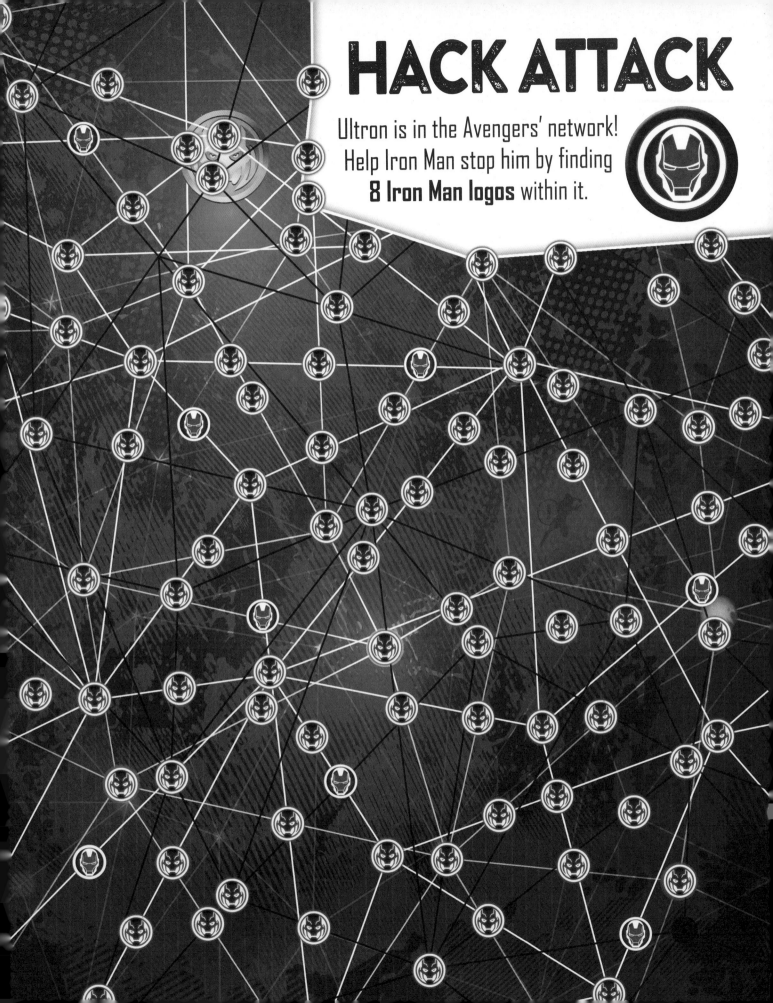

HACK ATTACK

Ultron is in the Avengers' network! Help Iron Man stop him by finding **8 Iron Man logos** within it.

CODEBREAKER CHALLENGE!

Well done! Now go back through the book and find all the hidden silhouettes. Once you have found them, write the corresponding letter on the page on the right to reveal the hidden message!

_ _ _ _ _

_ _ _ _ _

_ _ _ _ _

THE GOLDEN ICONS CHALLENGE!

Fancy taking on the Golden Icons challenge? Go back through the book and try to find all of the items below.